ADVENTURES OF SUPERMAN 463 Published monthly by DC Comics Inc., 666 Fifth Avenue, New York, NY 10103. POSTMASTER: Send address changes to ADVENTURES OF SUPERMAN, DC Comics Subscriptions, P.O. Box 0528, Baldwin, NY 11510. Annual subscription rate $9.00, Canada $14.00, all other foreign $21.00. U.S. funds only. Advertising Representative: Print Advertising Representatives, 355 Lexington Avenue, New York. NY 10017 (212) 949-6850. Printed in U.S.A. G-5428
DC Comics Inc. A Warner Bros. Company 2ND PRINTING

LESSEE... KEYSTONE CITY TO MT. RUSHMORE... SHOULDN'T TAKE MORE THAN A FEW SECONDS AT THIS SPEED!
COLD OUT HERE. GOOD THING THE AURA THAT PROTECTS ME FROM MY SPEED'S FRICTION WILL HELP AGAINST THE COLD.
-- BUT IT SURE WASN'T THIS!
LOOKS LIKE A WHOLE LOTTA POSTCARDS JUST BECAME OBSOLETE!
HEE HEE HEE! QUITE AN IMPROVEMENT, WOULDN'T YOU SAY, RED?
HEY... ALMOST DIDN'T SEE THIS LITTLE FLOATING MAN...
LITTLE FLOATING--?!
PRESIDENT!? SAYYY, THAT'S NOT A BAD IDEA! EH, MAYBE SOMEDAY...
ANYHOO, THE NAME'S MXYZPTLK--MR. TO YOU-- PURVEYOR OF GOOD TIMES AND CONSTANT THRILLS!
WHO'RE YOU?
FLASH. PLEASED TO MEET YOU.
I THINK.
FLASH, HUH? SO WHAT DOES A FLASH DO FOR KICKS?
WELL, BESIDES CAVING IN THE SKULLS OF PEOPLE WHO DESECRATE NATIONAL MONUMENTS I RUN FAST.
REAL FAST.
NO KIDDING?! FASTER THAN, SAY... SUPERMAN?

WHOA! TERRAIN'S GETTING PRETTY ROUGH AND SLIPPERY. AT LEAST I'M ALMOST THERE.
WILD! I DON'T KNOW WHAT I EXPECTED TO FIND HERE--
SPEED HILLS!
LOOK, PAL-- UNLESS YOU'RE THE PRESIDENT OF OZ, I DOUBT YOUR MUG BELONGS UP THERE!
DAN JURGENS-STORY AND PENCILS
ART THIBERT-FINISHES
ALBERT DE GUZMAN-LETTERS
GLENN WHITMORE-COLORS
JON PETERSON-ASSOCIATE EDITOR
MIKE CARLIN-EDITOR
SUPERMAN CREATED BY JERRY SIEGEL AND JOE SHUSTER
HOW SHOULD I KNOW? IT'S NOT LIKE WE'VE EVER RUN A RACE OR ANYTHING!
NOW IF YOU DON'T MIND, I WANT SOME ANSWERS!
A RACE?! SAYYY...
PLAY ALONG WITH ME, RED, AND I'LL MAKE YOU A STAR!
LOOK, I DON'T WANNA BE A STAR! I JUST WANT YOUR FACE OFF THAT MOUNTAIN!
GOOD, I KNEW YOU'D SEE IT MY WAY! NEXT STOP--
--METROPOLIS!
HEY, I DON'T WANT TO...
POOF
POOF

METROPOLIS.
AW, C'MON, CHIEF! WHAT DO YOU WANT FROM US?
SIMPLY PUT, AN INFORMATIVE, ENTERTAINING, WELL-ROUNDED NEWS MAGAZINE THAT BEATS THE COMPETITION.
NEWSTIME IS A GOOD, SOLID MAGAZINE BUT IT'S IN A RUT!
COLLIN THORNTON BROUGHT ME OVER TO GIVE NEWSTIME A DYNAMIC NEW LOOK AND THAT'S WHAT WE'RE GOING TO GIVE HIM!
THERE'S SOME PRETTY STIFF COMPETITION OUT THERE, MR. KENT!
AND THAT'S EXACTLY WHY WE HAVE TO BE BETTER!
NATIONAL NEWS WORLD REPORT
THIS WEEK! INFORMATION
TAKE THESE GUYS-- HARD INFORMATION WITH NO FLAIR OR PERSONALITY! IT'S LIKE READING A TELETYPE!
NEWS
THE MONSTER
WHO NEEDS IT? GET CREATIVE! TAKE CHANCES! AND ONE MORE THING--
--DON'T CALL ME CHIEF!
YES SIR!
YOU GOT IT!
WE'RE WITH YOU, CH--BOSS!
IMPRESSIVE. NOT ONLY ARE YOU AN EXCELLENT WRITER BUT YOU'RE QUITE THE MANAGER AS WELL! LOOKS LIKE I HIRED THE RIGHT MAN!
THANKS, COLLIN, BUT I DON'T THINK WE'LL REALLY KNOW THAT UNTIL WE GET A FEW ISSUES UNDER OUR BELT!
A'EEEE!
SOMEONE SCREAMING IN THE LOBBY!?
WE BETTER NOT HAVE MICE UP HERE AGAIN!
NEWSTIME
NEWSTIME
NEWSTIME

DO WE CALL SECURITY OR AN EXTERMINATOR?
NEITHER! OUR COMPUTER SYSTEM HAS GONE COMPLETELY BONKERS!
YOU GOTTA SEE IT TO BELIEVE IT!
WHY? OUR COMPUTERS HAVE CERTAINLY CRASHED BEFORE!
TIME
I DOUBT THEY EVER CRASHED DUE TO AN INTERDIMENSIONAL OVERLOAD, COLLIN!
I REALIZE THAT YOU JOURNALISTS TRYING TO BEAT A DEADLINE ARE PRETTY FRUSTRATED RIGHT NOW, BUT HANG WITH ME!
MR. MXYZPTLK IS ABOUT TO GIVE YOU THE BIGGEST STORY SINCE EVE MADE THAT DEAL WITH THE SNAKE!
JANUARY
ANNOUNCING THE EVENT OF ALL TIME! A CONTEST OF CHAMPIONS FILLED WITH POWER, SPEED DRAMA, SPEED, EXCITEMENT AND MOST OF ALL--
--TWO REALLY FAST GUYS!
THAT'S THAT MR. WHAT'S-IS-NAME--
WHAT'S THAT IMP BABBLING ABOUT, THIS TIME?
PART OF ME DOESN'T WANT TO KNOW!
OF COURSE I'M TALKING ABOUT A RACE!
A RACE BETWEEN SUPERMAN AND FLASH! THINK ABOUT IT, DREAM ABOUT IT--
--AND CATCH THE START OF IT LIVE IN JUST ONE HOUR AT THE METROPOLIS STADIUM!
COME ONE, COME ALL, ADMISSION IS FREE! HEE HEE HEE!
MUCH AS I'D LIKE TO IGNORE THIS, I CAN'T. IF SUPERMAN DOESN'T MAKE AN APPEARANCE--
--THERE'S NO TELLING WHAT MXYZPTLK WOULD DO!
MARA, CALL CARLISLE AND TELL HIM TO GET HIS CAMERA GEAR OVER TO THE STADIUM!
YES, SIR, MR. KENT!
MANAGING EDITORS DO NOT COVER STORIES THEMSELVES, KENT!
YOU HEARD HIM SAY IT WAS THE BIGGEST THING SINCE ORIGINAL SIN... THIS IS IMPORTANT!
HATED TO BRUSH THORNTON OFF LIKE THAT, BUT CLARK KENT HAS TO GET OUT OF THE OFFICE--
--IF SUPERMAN'S GOING TO FLY!

LISTEN, I DON'T CARE WHAT YOU SAY! SUPERMAN'S GOT THIS IN THE BAG!
NO WAY, POPS! FLASH BY A MILE!
NO ONE CAN OUTRUN THE BIG "S"!
YOU KIDDIN' ME? FLASH'LL BLOW HIM AWAY!
VS.
METROPOLIS STADIUM
WHO CARES WHO WINS? OUGHTA BE A GOOD SHOW!
HEY, MY BOOKIE CARES PLENTY WHO WINS!
A RACE?!
BETWEEN SUPERMAN AND ME?!
ARE YOU OUT OF YOUR FREAKING MIND?!
AWW, C'MON, RED! JUST LOOK AT ALL THE PEOPLE HERE WHO WANNA SEE YOU WIN!
FORGET IT, SHORTY!
I'M NOT SOME STUPID PUPPET THAT'S GONNA JUMP JUST CUZ YOU'RE PULLING THE STRINGS!
IF YOU THINK I'M GONNA WASTE MY TIME RACING SUPERMAN--
--YOU'RE NUTS!
GATE F
SIGH
SNAP
HEY!
HEE HEE. NOW, WHY DON'T YOU PLAY ALONG BEFORE I TURN YOU INTO A TURTLE--
--OR SOMETHING SLOWER?
POOF
HOW ABOUT YOU LEAVE INSTEAD?

GET THROWN OUT OF THE FIFTH DIMENSION FOR SMUGGLING WHOOPEE CUSHIONS AGAIN, MXYZPTLK?
AHH, YOU WOUND ME, SOOPEY! CAN'T YOU SEE THAT I'M PRESENTING YOU WITH THE OPPORTUNITY OF A LIFETIME?
ISN'T THE CHANCE TO PROVE YOUR SUPERIORITY WORTH A HANDSHAKE?
IS THIS CLOWN REALLY A BUDDY OF YOURS?
THIS CLOWN IS JUST THAT-- AND NOTHING MORE.
NOW, IS THAT ANY WAY TO TALK TO THE MAN WHO CAN CLAIM THE FALL OF THE ROMAN EMPIRE ON HIS RESUMÉ?
ARGUE ALL YOU WANT, SUPESTER, BUT YOU KNOW IF I HANG AROUND EARTH LONG I'M LIKELY TO SET OFF AT LEAST FOUR NUCLEAR CONFLICTS.
THAT MEANS YOU SIMPLY HAVE TO GET ME TO RETURN TO MY OWN DIMENSION.
AND IF YOU WANT A SHOT AT THAT--
--YOU GOTTA DANCE TO THE TUNE I PLAY!
SO WHY NOT BE A SPORT AND RACE SPEEDY GONZALEZ OVER THERE? BEAT HIM--
--AND I'M OUTTA YOUR HAIR FOR ANOTHER NINETY DAYS!
BUT IF YOU'D RATHER I STAAYYED...
OKAY, OKAY. BUT WHAT MAKES YOU THINK IT WILL BE MUCH OF A CONTEST?
WORD HAS IT THAT WALLY HERE'S NOT QUITE AS FAST AS THE ORIGINAL FLASH, BARRY ALLEN WAS--
--AND EVEN THOUGH WE'VE NEVER RACED I KIND OF JUST ASSUMED...
HEY, WAIT A MINUTE!
I MEAN, WHEN YOU GET DOWN TO IT, WHAT WE REALLY HAVE HERE IS A RACE BETWEEN SUPERMAN AND KID FLASH!
ALL RIGHT, THAT'S ENOUGH!

SURE, YOU MIGHT BE ABLE TO MOVE MOUNTAINS AND FLY--
--BUT THAT DOESN'T NECESSARILY MAKE YOU FASTER THAN ME!
I SAY PUT UP OR SHUT UP, SUPERMAN!
LOOK, I DIDN'T MEAN TO INSULT YOU, FLASH! I JUST ASSUMED I WAS NATURALLY FASTER!
LET'S SEE WHAT YOU SAY WHEN I DUST YOU AT THE FINISH LINE!
LADEEEZ AND GENTLEMEN, THE RACE IS ON! HEE HEE HEE!
NOT SO FAST, TINY! WHAT DO I GET OUT OF ALL THIS?
BESIDES THE SATISFACTION OF BEATING OLD SUPES YOU GET A PRIZE SELECTED JUST FOR YOU!
A VERY SPECIAL PRIZE!
NUTS--WHO CARES ABOUT A PRIZE? ALL I KNOW IS THAT IF I BACK OUT OF THIS RACE--
--THE WHOLE WORLD IS GONNA FIGURE ME FOR A WIMPY WEENIE!
JUST HOPE SUPERMAN DOESN'T WHIP ME TOO BAD...
HEE HEE--NOW THAT WE HAVE OUR LINE-UP STRAIGHTENED OUT WE CAN START!
GENTLEMEN--
--START YOUR ENGINES!
WHAT'S WITH THE CARPET?
GROUND RULES, FLASHEROO! THIS IS ACTUALLY THE TRACK YOU TWO WILL RUN THE RACE ON!
NOT ONLY WILL IT MARK THE COURSE FOR YOU, BUT IT'LL HELP ENSURE THAT SUPES DOESN'T FLY!

ONCE AROUND THE WORLD, GENTLEMEN! AND STEP ON IT!
ON YOUR MARK--
--GET SET--
BLAM
--AND GO--
--GO--
--GO!
SEE YOU AT THE FINISH LINE, SUPERMAN!
FLASH
GO FLASH
BETTER HURRY, FLASH! I WON'T WAIT LONG FOR YOU!
CAN'T BELIEVE I'M DOING THIS! BUT IF IT GETS MXYZPTLK OFF MY BACK IT'S WORTH THE PRICE!
THAT IMP IS DANGEROUS! THE LAST TIME HE WAS HERE HE TORE UP HALF OF METROPOLIS!
LOOK AT THE GUY! SO POWERFUL--SO CONFIDENT--
--IT'S PROBABLY NEVER OCCURRED TO HIM THAT HE JUST MIGHT LOSE!
HURRY IT UP, LOIS!
THE RACE HAS ALREADY STARTED!
YOU ARE GOING TO WATCH IT, AREN'T YA?
BE RIGHT THERE, SIS. WHO'S LEADING?
EVEN-STEVEN SO FAR!
OH, I DON'T KNOW, LUCE. I'VE BEEN FEELING SORT OF OUT OF IT ALL WEEK.
I'VE FELT LIKE THIS SINCE CLARK LEFT THE PLANET!
WOW, FOR A SUPERMAN FAN, YOU DON'T SEEM TOO ENTHUSIASTIC!

WOW, LO, I NEVER REALIZED YOU WERE SO HUNG UP ON THE GUY. HE JUST DOESN'T SEEM LIKE YOUR TYPE.
YOU KNOW, HE REALLY IS A PRETTY DECENT GUY! AND EVEN THOUGH I WAS KIND OF HARD ON HIM AT FIRST--
--CLARK WAS ALWAYS THERE FOR ME WHEN I NEEDED HIM!
GUESS I WAS A LITTLE OBSESSED WITH SUPERMAN AND MY CAREER AND JOSÉ AND EVERYTHING TO REALLY NOTICE HIM.
AND NOW HE'S GONE.
"WE'RE HERE LIVE WITH MR. MASON TROLLBRIDGE, WIDELY REGARDED TO BE A CLOSE ASSOCIATE OF FLASH'S. WHO DO YOU LIKE IN THE BIG RACE, MASON?"
"WELL, I FIGURE FLASH'S ODDS ARE PRETTY GOOD SO LONG AS WE CAN GET PEOPLE TO HELP US OUT BY GIVING FLASH FOOD ALONG THE COURSE. KIND OF LIKE MARATHON RUNNERS GET, YOU KNOW."
"THANKS, MASON. WE'RE SWITCHING TO A REMOTE SECTION OF NORTH DAKOTA WHERE HUNDREDS OF PEOPLE ARE DOING JUST AS MR. TROLLBRIDGE SUGGESTS. REPORTS FROM SOUTH DAKOTA SAY THE RUNNERS ARE APPROACHING--"
"--YES... HERE THEY COME AND... WOOOO... THERE THEY GO!"
THANKS FOR THE OFFER, BUT I DON'T NEED ANY FOOD!
GREAT! JUST WHAT THE DOCTOR ORDERED!
WHY DON'T YOU HAVE TO EAT, SUPERMAN? YOU'RE EXPENDING ENERGY SAME AS ME!
MY KRYPTONIAN CELLS ABSORB AND BURN THE ENERGY OF THE SUN!
GUESS I JUST "EAT" IN A MORE DIRECT FASHION!
YA HOO-- NECK AND NECK, EH?
REMEMBER, I'LL BE WATCHING ALL THE WAY! AND IF ANYBODY CHEATS--
--WHAMMO!
IS THAT TWERP FOR REAL?
UNFORTUNATELY...

¡SIGH¡--THIS IS ALREADY GETTING BORING! MAYBE I SHOULD LIVEN THINGS UP!
SO, MXYZPTLK IS REALLY FROM ANOTHER DIMENSION?
YEAH. HE SHOWS UP EVERY NOW AND THEN LOOKING FOR FUN... BY WAY OF CREATING HAVOC! AND SINCE HIS POWERS DEFY OUR DIMENSIONAL LAWS--
--MY OWN POWERS ARE PRETTY MUCH USELESS AGAINST HIM.
NO WONDER YOU HAVE TO MAKE BARGAINS TO GET RID OF--
YEEOWW!
THIS FREAKY COURSE HAS COME ALIVE--
--LIKE IT'S TRYING TO SHAKE US OFF!
IT'S MXYZPTLK'S WAY OF MAKING THINGS MORE INTERESTING!
WHY ELSE WOULD THE COURSE RUN ALONG THE FLOOR OF THE BERING STRAIT?
I CAN'T RUN UNDERWATER! WHAT'LL I DO?
ONE CHANCE--I'M GONNA TRY RUNNING ON THE SURFACE... LIKE A ROCK SKIPPING THE WAVES!
¡UHHH¡--LOSING BALANCE--LOOK OUT!

NEVER REALLY TRIED RUNNING THIS FAR OR TESTING MY ENDURANCE BEFORE--
--BUT I'M SURE I CAN BEAT FLASH! AFTER ALL, HE'S ONLY A HUMAN!
OOF!--THE TECHNIQUE MAY NOT LOOK PRETTY BUT IT GOT THE JOB DONE!
HEY, SHOULDN'T YOU BE DISQUALIFIED FOR LEAVING THE COURSE?
WRONGO, SUPES! FLASHEROO'S TOOTSIES NEVER LEFT GOOD OL' EARTH--HE WAS IN CONTACT WITH TERRA INFIRMA THE WHOLE TIME!
THEREFORE, AS THE COMPLETELY IMPARTIAL REFEREE OF THIS EVENT, I'M NOT GONNA PENALIZE HIM JUST 'CAUSE HE CAN'T MAKE LIKE A FISH WHEN YOU CAN!
AND ACCORDING TO THE RULES, WHICH I'M MAKING UP AS YOU GO ALONG, FROM NOW ON YOU'RE ON SEPARATE TRACKS!
JEEZ, THANKS, MIXXY. YOU'RE A REAL PEACH!
BARRY ALWAYS SPOKE SO HIGHLY OF SUPERMAN--MADE HIM OUT TO BE SO POWERFUL THAT I WAS ALMOST INTIMIDATED BY HIM!
BUT WE'RE STILL EVEN UP! MAYBE I REALLY CAN WIN THIS THING!
HEE HEE, I MUST ADMIT THAT I DO LOVE DRIVING SUPES NUTSO!
WHOA-HO-HO, WHAT'S THAT? DO MY PEEPERS DECEIVE ME--
--OR DO I SEE SOMEONE ELSE I KNOW?
OUR SATELLITE SENSORS TRACKED THE METEOR TO THIS APPROXIMATE LOCATION, SIR!
EXCELLENT. IF THERE IS ANY KRYPTONITE EMBEDDED IN THE METEOR WE'LL EXTRACT IT AND RETREAT.
EVEN SOMEONE OF MY STATURE WOULD HAVE TROUBLE EXPLAINING MY PRESENCE TO SOVIET AUTHORITIES!
OLD FRIEND, OLD BUDDY, OLD PAL, IS IT REALLY YOU?

YES, YES IT IS! LEX LUTHOR!
ALL YOU HAD TO DO WAS ASK AND I WOULD GLADLY HAVE GIVEN YOU A RINGSIDE SEAT!
GET AWAY FROM ME, YOU IGNOMINIOUS LITTLE TOAD!
I DON'T KNOW WHAT YOU'RE BABBLING ABOUT AND I DON'T CARE! AND IF YOU PLAN TO HARASS ME AS YOU DID BEFORE I'LL KILL YOU!
GADZOOKS! HOW CAN THIS BE?
HOW CAN THE GREAT LEX LUTHOR NOT KNOW OF THE GREAT RACE!?
MY CONCERNS ARE MY OWN, MXYZPTLK. LEAVE US!
NO SIGNS OF ANY KRYPTONITE IN THE AREA, SIR. WE MIGHT AS WELL LEAVE.
KRYPTONITE, HMM? Y'KNOW, LEX, I'D LIKE TO MAKE UP FOR THE TROUBLES I CAUSED YOU IN THE PAST!
I WAS GONNA GIVE THIS SPECIAL PRIZE TO FLASH--
--BUT I THINK MAYBE YOU COULD USE IT MORE.
SNAP
WHATCHA THINK? PEACE? PEACE OF KRYPTONITE?
GOOD THING WE HAVE THESE RADIATION SUITS ON BOSS. IT'S NOT GREEN K, BUT THAT ROCK IS PRETTY RICH!
WRONG COLOR? WELL, IT WAS A GOOD GUESS-- NO?
MXYZPTLK, YOU ARE A FOOL! GET THAT WORTHLESS CHUNK OF POISON OUT OF HERE!
WORTHLESS, HUH?
OH, FUDGE.
LET'S MOVE ON TO THE NEXT SITE, REYNOLDS!
ONLY SUPERMAN RAISES MY IRE MORE THAN THAT IMP!
LOVE TO JOIN YOU, LEXXY, BUT I'VE GOT A RACE TO GET BACK TO--

"--AND THOSE TWO CHUCKLEHEADS ARE PROBABLY IN THE SOVIET UNION'S URAL MOUNTAIN RANGE, BY NOW."
WHEW-- I'M ACTUALLY STARTING TO FEEL A BIT WINDED!
EVEN THOUGH I HAVE SUPER HUMAN POWERS I'M NOT TRAINED AS A RUNNER AND THIS IS MORE PHYSICAL WORK THAN FLYING TO THE MOON!
AT LEAST I'VE MOVED OUT FRONT! THE LACK OF AIR AT THIS ALTITUDE IS REALLY HARD ON FLASH!
MAN, LOOK AT BIG-BLUE GO! I GOTTA KEEP BREATHING UP HERE WHILE HE'S STILL GOT A LUNG FULL OF THE GOOD STUFF!
SHOULD'VE KNOWN THAT I WAS OUT-CLASSED FROM THE START-- THAT I HAD NO CHANCE!
AND NOW THE WHOLE WORLD IS GONNA SEE ME LOSE--
--UNLESS I CAN REALLY POUR IT ON... GET A SECOND WIND AND PROVE I DESERVE TO WEAR BARRY'S UNIFORM!
AMAZING! FLASH IS STARTING TO CLOSE THE GAP DESPITE THE LACK OF OXYGEN!
HAVE TO STAY IN FRONT--NOT JUST TO GET RID OF MXYZPTLK--
--BUT BECAUSE I'D REALLY HATE TO LOSE!
SKRUNNNNK
YEOWW! NOW WHAT?

HI, GUYS! I'M BAAAACK!
HEY, PUT ME DOWN! I'M RUNNING YOUR BLASTED RACE-- WHAT MORE DO YOU WANT?
HE'S JUST TRYING TO REMIND US WHO'S IN CHARGE OF THIS SHOW!
HEE HEE HEE! NOW, THIS IS ENTERTAINMENT!
THINK SO, HUH?
WELL, LET'S SEE HOW YOU HOLD UP TO A FEW HUNDRED THOUSAND BLOWS!
CHOKKA CHOKKA CHOKK
KRA-KOW
I'VE BEEN WAITING TO DO SOMETHING LIKE THIS ALL DAY!
WAY TO GO, S-MAN!

SHALL WE CONTINUE?
IF YOU THINK YOU CAN STILL KEEP UP-- LET'S DO IT!
PARIS, FRANCE.
STATUS REPORT, METAMORPHO!
SO FAR, SO GOOD, CAP! TWINKLE TOES IS REALLY HANGIN' IN THERE!
GO, FLASH, GO! FOR HONOR-- FOR GLORY--
--FOR THE SAKE OF JUSTICE LEAGUE EUROPE--BEAT SUPERMAN!
PERSONALLY, I HOPE SUPERMAN RUNS HIM RIGHT OUT OF THOSE WIMPY, WINGED BOOTS.
NEW YORK, NEW YORK.
THE RACE PROCEEDS AS EXPECTED, MR. MIRACLE. THE CONTESTANTS ARE DEPARTING THE SOVIET UNION EVEN AS WE SPEAK.
WAY TO KICK, FLASH! RUN LIKE YOU'VE NEVER RUN BEFORE!
BOOSTER, ARE YOU CRAZY? WE'RE SUPPOSED TO BE CHEERING SUPERMAN HERE!
WE DON'T WANT SOME REPRESENTATIVE FROM THAT GANG OF SECOND-RATE IMITATORS TO WIN!
GIMME A BREAK, BEETLE! I GOT A THOUSAND BUCKS ON FLASH AT FOUR TO ONE ODDS!
EGYPT.
‹DO THEY APPROACH?›
‹YES, PRAISE ALLAH! I BELIEVE I SEE THEM!›
‹FAH! IT IS MORE LIKELY A SANDSTORM!›

< NO, INFIDEL! IT TRULY IS THE SPECIAL ONES! >
THANKS A LOT, FRIEND! I'M TIRED ENOUGH -- WITHOUT THIS FOOD I'D NEVER FINISH THE RACE!
EVERY TIME I THINK I HAVE YOU BEAT YOU MANAGE TO BOUNCE BACK!
HEY, IF I COULDN'T DO THAT THEY WOULDN'T CALL ME FLASH!
YOU MIGHT WEAR THE CLOTHES BUT YOU'RE NOT THE HUMBLE MAN BARRY WAS!
WHY CAN'T ANY OF YOU OLD GUYS GO FIVE MINUTES WITHOUT MENTIONING HIM?
HE WAS A GOOD MAN, WALLY. YOU'VE GOT A LOT TO LIVE UP--
BRKAMM
...UHN!... THAT TUNNEL--
--IT WAS JUST AN ILLUSION! REALLY SOLID ROCK--!
KNOCKED THE WIND OUT OF ME--CAN'T BREATHE--TOO TIRED...
LOOKS LIKE THE WHOLE CAVE COLLAPSED AND BURIED SUPERMAN!
IF IT TAKES HALF AS LONG AS IT LOOKS LIKE IT WILL FOR HIM TO DIG OUT I'VE GOT THIS SUCKER LOCKED UP!

JEEZ, WHAT IF SOMETHING'S REALLY WRONG, THOUGH, AND HE CAN'T DIG OUT?
STRONG AS HE IS, HE HIT THAT ROCK HARD AND FAST! EVEN IF HE IS INVULNERABLE-- HE'S BEEN RUNNING FOR A WHILE... PROBABLY PRETTY BEAT TO START WITH.
BESIDES, IF MXYZPTLK RIGGED THAT THING WITH HIS PSEUDO-MAGIC, WHO KNOWS HOW IT AFFECTED SUPERMAN?
NO CHOICE.

GOTTA GET MOVIN'--
--AND USE MY SPEED--
--ALONG WITH A LITTLE ELBOW GREASE--
--TO DIG DOWN TO THE BOTTOM--
--AND GET HIM OUT OF THERE BEFORE THE SAND FLEAS START CRAWLING UP HIS CAPE!

WELCOME BACK TO THE LAND OF THE LIVING!
YEAH--LOOKS LIKE MXYZPTLK IS OUT TO RIG THE RACE!
SPEAKING OF WHICH, I'M SURPRISED YOU'RE STILL AROUND!

HEY, EVERY NOW AND THEN I CAN'T HELP MYSELF. I DO A GOOD DEED.
RIGHT. LOOK, YOU PROBABLY DON'T WANT TO HEAR THIS, BUT I THINK BARRY WOULD BE PRETTY HAPPY TO SEE YOU IN HIS GEAR.

MAYBE IT'S TIME YOU ACCEPT THAT.
UM... YEAH, WELL... WHAT SAY WE GET MOVING--
--AND GET BACK TO THE RACE? I STILL DO INTEND TO WIN.
SO DO I.

WHEW--CAN'T BELIEVE THIS PACE! NEVER RUN THIS FAST--THIS FAR BEFORE--
--AND WE STILL GOTTA GO THROUGH SPAIN AND ACROSS THE ATLANTIC!
EXHAUSTED--LEGS ARE LIKE SPAGHETTI! FLASH IS FASTER--STRONGER THAN I THOUGHT!
AND I FEEL LIKE--I MIGHT NOT EVEN BE ABLE TO FINISH!
HOW ABOUT THAT, JAY? LOOKS LIKE OUR YOUNG FELLOW IS DOING US PROUD!
C'MON, WALLY! SHOW LIL'OL' CONNIE HOW MUCH YOU LOVE HER!
WOW, LOIS! THOSE GUYS ARE STILL IN A DEAD HEAT!
AND I THOUGHT FOR SURE THAT SUPERMAN WAS A CINCH TO WIN!
ANY SIGN OF THEM YET, CHIEF?
SHOULDN'T BE LONG, JIMMY!
I HOPE THEY HURRY--I'M FREEZING OUT HERE!
BOY, ISN'T THAT SUMTHIN? ALL THE WAY AROUND THE WORLD...
RUN, CLARK, RUN!
WONDER HOW LOIS WILL FEEL ABOUT HIM IF FLASH KICKS HIS BUTT?
GOODNESS GRACIOUS! THEY'RE RUNNING AT SEVERAL TIMES THE SPEED OF SOUND!
WHERE THE DEVIL IS KENT? THE BIGGEST STORY OF THE YEAR--AND MY MANAGING EDITOR DISAPPEARS!

YIPPEE KIII--YAYYY, GENTLEMEN! YOU ARE NOW ENTERING THE HOME STRETCH!
WHO WILL WIN?
WHO WILL LOSE?
STAY TUNED--FILM AT ELEVEN! HEE HEE!
MXYZPTLK--
--SHUT THE HECK UP!
SPALOOSH
STILL HALF THE ATLANTIC TO GO--AND I CAN'T SHAKE HIM!
NEVER THOUGHT I COULD EVEN RUN THIS ¦PANT¦--FAST! AND I STILL CAN'T PASS HIM!
LUNGS BURNING--LEGS ACHING--SO TIRED--¦PANT¦--I JUST WANT TO DROP!
EXPECTED TO BE ON CRUISE CONTROL BY NOW--BUT I MUST GO FASTER!
CAN'T BELIEVE--PANT--I'M STILL RUNNING NECK AND NECK WITH SUPERMAN!
BUT I FEEL LIKE I'VE GOT NUTHIN' LEFT--AND HE'S SPEEDING UP!
BLAST IT, SUPERMAN! WHY DON'T YOU DROP?!
PACK IT IN, FLASH! GIVE IT UP!
CAN'T YOU SEE I HAVE TO GET RID OF MXYZPTLK?

LIKE TWO NORMAL LONG-DISTANCE RUNNERS THEY BOTH HIT "THE WALL" LONG AGO.
EACH BREATH SEARS THEIR LUNGS.
EACH STRIDE IS AGONY.
YET THEY GO EVEN FASTER...
...NEITHER ONE ABLE TO GIVE IN.
CAN'T-- WON'T QUIT--
GOTTA PUSH HARDER!
CAN'T BREATH-- BUT I GOTTA KEEP IT UP AND BEAT THIS GUY!
GREAT CAESAR'S GHOST, OLSEN! AFTER ALL THIS, THEY'RE TIED!
NO, CHIEF-- LOOK! SOMEONE'S PULLING OUT FRONT! THE WINNER IS--
YES!
I DID IT!
I BEAT SUPERMAN!
FLASH?
FLASH WON?!

CONSARN IT! FLASH WON!
I DON'T KNOW HOW THE HE DID IT, BUT HE WON!
'N' NOW I GOTTA GO HOME! THANKS FER NUTHIN', LUTHOR!
I DON'T GET IT! I LOST!
LAST TIME I WAS HERE LUTHOR LIED TO ME-- HE SHOWED ME HOW TO SET UP A FALSE DEAL!
AND SINCE I KNEW YOU WERE A SHOE-IN TO WIN THE RACE, I WAS ONLY PLANNIN' TO LEAVE IF FLASH WON!
I'M A BAAAD LIAR!
SOMEHOW YOU SAW THROUGH MY TRICK AND THREW THE RACE!
I MUST'VE MISSED SOME SUBTLETY IN LUTHOR'S TECHNIQUE!
SO EVEN THOUGH YOU LOST THE STUPID RACE, SUPERDOPE--
--YOU WIN BECAUSE I HAVE TO ABIDE BY MY OWN RULES AND GO!
I SHOULD HAVE KNOWN IT WOULDN'T BE EASY TO LIE TO MYSELF!
BUT I'M GOING TO PRACTICE--AND THEN I'LL BE BACK!
POOF
THANK GOD!
DAMN IT, SUPERMAN--
--YOU KNEW! YOU FOLDED AND LET ME WIN!
ARE YOU KIDDING ME? -HUFF- I HAD NO IDEA WHAT HE WAS UP TO! -PUFF- I GAVE THAT RACE EVERYTHING I HAD ...AND MORE!
YOU WON IT FAIR AND SQUARE, PAL!
I'D SAY YOU'RE PROBABLY THE FASTEST MAN ALIVE!
WELL, HOW ABOUT THAT!
THERE'S ONLY ONE PROBLEM!
WHAT'S THAT?
THAT LITTLE TWERP LEFT WITHOUT GIVING ME MY PRIZE!
END

SUPERMAN 11 Published monthly by DC Comics Inc., 666 Fifth Avenue, New York, NY 10103. POSTMASTER: Send address changes to SUPERMAN, DC Comics Inc., Subscription Dept. P.O. Box 1981, New York, NY 10185. Annual subscription rate $9.00. Outside U.S.A. $11.00 in U.S. funds.

TIRED FEET?
ALLOW ME, MISS LANE.
HEY, WAIT! I DON'T EVEN KNO-O-O-OOOHHHHH!
YOU... DO... THAT... VERY WELL, MISTER...
MISTER...?
I DON'T BELIEVE I CAUGHT THE NAME...?
I DON'T BELIEVE I THREW IT.
DeROY IS THE NAME, MISS LANE. BEN DeROY.
I'VE COME TO TAKE YOU OUT TO LUNCH.
LUNCH...?
OH, BUT I...
LOIS...
YOU HAVE A LUNCH DATE TODAY.
WITH ME!
I HADN'T FORGOTTEN, CLARK.
I WAS JUST ABOUT TO TELL MR. DeROY...
...THAT I'D BE ABSOLUTELY DELIGHTED TO HAVE LUNCH WITH HIM!
2

WHAT IN THE...??
DON'T LET HER GET YOU DOWN, CLARKIE.
C'MON.
NO POINT WASTING A LOVELY AFTERNOON.
I'LL BUY YOU LUNCH!
OH--ER--CAT!
ER--YES. THANKS. THANKS VERY MUCH.
THAT... DIDN'T SEEM AT ALL LIKE THE LOIS I KNOW.
"WHAT COULD'VE GOTTEN INTO HER?"
DID YOU ENJOY THAT, MISS LANE?
IT WAS FRANKLY FABULOUS, MR. DEROY.
EXCEPT...
EXCUSE ME. THIS HAPPENS TO BE THE NO SMOKING SECTION, FELLA.
SO? THIS ALSO HAPPENS TO BE A FREE COUNTRY, MISS BUTT-IN-SKI!
I'LL SMOKE ANYWHERE I DAMN WELL PLEASE!
AND IF YOU DON'T LIKE IT, YOU CAN...
... MOVE...!!!

IT'S NEARLY FOUR, MISS LANE.
I SUPPOSE I SHOULD GET YOU BACK TO THE OFFICE.
ER... YES. I SUPPOSE SO!
ODD... EVEN WITH THE WINDOWS OPEN IT'S BECOME SUDDENLY HOT IN HERE!
MY HAND!
AHHGH!!
AHHGH!!!
MY HAND!!!
IT'S FORTY BLOCKS TO THE DAILY PLANET BUILDING.
SHALL I HAIL A TAXI?
NO.
IT'S SUCH A BEAUTIFUL AFTERNOON I FEEL LIKE WALKING.
FUNNY. ONLY A FEW HOURS AGO MY FEET WERE KILLING ME.
NOW I FEEL AS IF I'M WALKING ON AIR!
YES...
AS YOU SAY...
FUNNY...
MIKEY!!
WILL YOU PLEASE PICK THAT THING UP!!
NO! NO! GOR-KA WANNA WALK!
GOR-KA WANNA WALK!!
I'M NOT BEING A VERY GOOD REPORTER.
FOUR HOURS I'VE BEEN WITH YOU, AND I DON'T EVEN KNOW WHERE YOU'RE FROM!
OH...HERE AND THERE.
YONDER, LET'S SAY.
YES...
YONDER...

"YONDER"?
YES ..YES, I SUPPOSE THAT WILL DO.
IT HAS JUST THE RIGHT TOUCH OF MYSTERY..
OF ROMANCE...
RRRRR
MIKEY!!
OH, GOD, NO!!
NOOOOO!!
ROMANCE...
AH, YES. I'M SO GLAD YOU BROUGHT THAT UP, MISS LANE...
YOU SEE... THERE'S SOMETHING I WANT TO ASK YOU...
RAAARRR
MEANWHILE...
I TELL YA, MR. OLSEN. IT WAS THE CRAZIEST THING I EVER SEEN!
SALE
LADIES!! DON'T MISS OUR ANNUAL 3-DAY WHITE EVENT!
40-50% OFF ALL SHEETS & TOWELS
AND THIS WAS JUST THIS MORNING, YOU SAID?
RIGHT AFTER YOU OPENED?
YEP.
WE ALREADY HAD A PRETTY FULL STORE, WHAT WITH THIS BEING TH' FIRST DAY OF OUR BIG WHITE SALE.
40% OFF
WHEN ALL OF A SUDDEN...
ALE
SALE
5

"WELL... JUST LIKE THAT TH' WHOLE STORE WENT CRAZY!
"THERE WAS SHEETS AN' LINEN AN' TOWELS FLYING EVERY WHICH WAY.'
"AN' RIGHT IN THE MIDDLE OF IT ALL..."
WELL, THAT WAS STIMULATING...
BUT I REALLY CAME HERE FOR A MUCH BIGGER GAME.
GOOD MORNING, LADIES!!
SALE
SAL
HUH! SURE SOUNDS LIKE THERE WAS A LOT MORE TO THIS THAN JUST SOME PUBLICITY STUNT FOR A WHITE SALE.
TIME TO CALL OUT THE BIG GUNS, I'D SAY.
ZEEEEZEEEEEEE
THAT'S WHAT I WAS HOPIN' YOU'D DO WHEN I CALLED TH' DAILY PLANET!
STILL WAITING FOR LOIS TO COME BACK FROM LUNCH, CLARKIE?
PUT HER OUT OF YOUR MIND, WHY DON'T YOU?
LET ME COME UP TO YOUR APARTMENT THIS EVENING AND I'LL BAKE YOU UP SOME OF MY WORLD CLASS LASAGNA.
WELL... THAT DOES SOUND TEMPTING, CAT...
BUT I'M QUITE WORRIED ABOUT LOIS. TO HAVE ACTED SO STRANGELY...
AND THEN TO BE GONE ALL AFTERNOON...
I REALLY THINK I SHOULD...
UH-OH... JIMMY'S SIGNAL WATCH!
CLARK!
SORRY, CAT.
HAVE TO TAKE A RAIN CHECK ON THAT LASAGNA.
SOMETHING... JUST CAME UP.
SOMETHING THAT MAY BE A JOB...
MUG-R-US

FOR SUPERMAN!
NOW... WHERE'S JIMMY? THE HYPERSONIC SIGNAL IS COMING FROM THE NORTH-WEST.
A QUICK SCAN WITH MY TELESCOPIC VISION SHOULD...
GREAT SCOTT!!
THAT'S NOT WHAT JIMMY'S SIGNALLING ME ABOUT...
BUT IT'S SOMETHING I'VE GOT TO TAKE CARE OF.
AND NOW!!
THUMP
THUMP
THUMP
OKAY, BIG BOY, PLAYTIME'S OVER!
LET'S SEE IF WE CAN'T FIND OUT WHERE YOU ESCAPED FROM.
PRESUMABLY A CIRCUS, SINCE ZOOS DON'T GENERALLY DYE THEIR ANIMALS.

POING!
?!?
KRAK
WHAT IN THE NAME OF...??
THIS WAS A LIVING, BREATHING, FULL-SIZED GORILLA!
I TOUCHED IT!
SMELLED IT!
WHAAAH!!
HE BROKE GOR-KA! HE BROKE GOR-KA!!
SH-SHUT UP, MIKEY!!
MA'M...
THIS TOY... IT BELONGS TO YOU?
WHAT HAPPENED HERE?
I... I... I DON'T KNOW, SUPERMAN. WE... WE WERE JUST WALKING... IT WAS RAINING...
I REMEMBER... WE'D JUST PASSED THIS GUY... THIS GREAT BIG GUY IN A WHITE SUIT...
AND... HE WAS WITH A WOMAN WHO LOOKED LIKE...
"LOIS LANE..."
M-MARRY YOU??

BUT... MR. DEROY, WE HARDLY...
...KNOW...
OH, YES! YES!!
OH, MR. DEROY, YOU'VE MADE ME THE HAPPIEST WOMAN...
SAY...
HOLD ON A MINUTE!
WHERE HAS MY MIND BEEN?
WHY, SHE'S MUCH PRETTIER THAN YOU!
WH-WHAT..??
LOOKS AT THOSE EYES! THOSE LIPS!
THOSE...
WELL, JUST LOOK AT HER!
IS...,THIS SOME KIND OF JOKE?
THAT... THAT'S A MANNEQUIN!
IT'S NOT ALIVE!!
NOT ALIVE...?
OH, BUT YOU'RE WRONG, MISS LANE.
SHE'S VERY MUCH ALIVE...

ALIVE...
AND EVERYTHING ANY MAN COULD WANT!
OH, BEN HONEY! Y'ALL DO SAY TH' SWEETEST THAINGS!
AND NOW, IF YOU'LL EXCUSE US, MISS LANE, WE...
BEN, HONEY! WAIT! Y'ALL CAIN'T JEST STROLL OFF WITH ME!
THAT'D BE STEALIN'!
BUT...
BUT...
YOU'RE RIGHT, OF COURSE. PERHAPS...
PERHAPS AN EXCHANGE WOULD BE MORE ACCEPTABLE!
NO SIGN OF LOIS ANYWHERE!
AND THAT BEN DEROY CHARACTER SEEMS TO HAVE FADED INTO THE OZONE, TOO!
A WOMAN'S SCREAM...
COMING FROM STACY'S DEPARTMENT STORE.
YES THIS IS STACY'S
MISS...?
WHAT IS IT? WHAT'S WRONG?
TH'...TH'... TH' WINDOW DISPLAY!!
I WAS S'POSED TO CHANGE THE SETUP T'DAY...
BUT... BUT...

OH MY GOD!!
LOIS!!
SHE'S BEEN TRANSFORMED INTO A MANNEQUIN!!
BUT...
SHE'S WARM...
STILL ALIVE!
WHAT IN BLAZES IS GOING ON AROUND HERE?
FIRST THAT GORILLA...
NOW LOIS...
YAHHHH
HERE WE GO AGAIN!
MISS...CALL THE POLICE!
GET MAGGIE SAWYER'S SPECIAL CRIMES UNIT DOWN HERE!
Y-YESSIR!
LOOR
RECTORY
MAGGIE'S TEAM CAN PROTECT LOIS UNTIL I CAN FIND SOME WAY TO RESTORE HER TO HUMAN FORM...
IF I CAN FIND A WAY!
NOW...WHERE DID THAT OTHER SCREAM COME FROM? A MAN'S SCREAM THIS TIME...

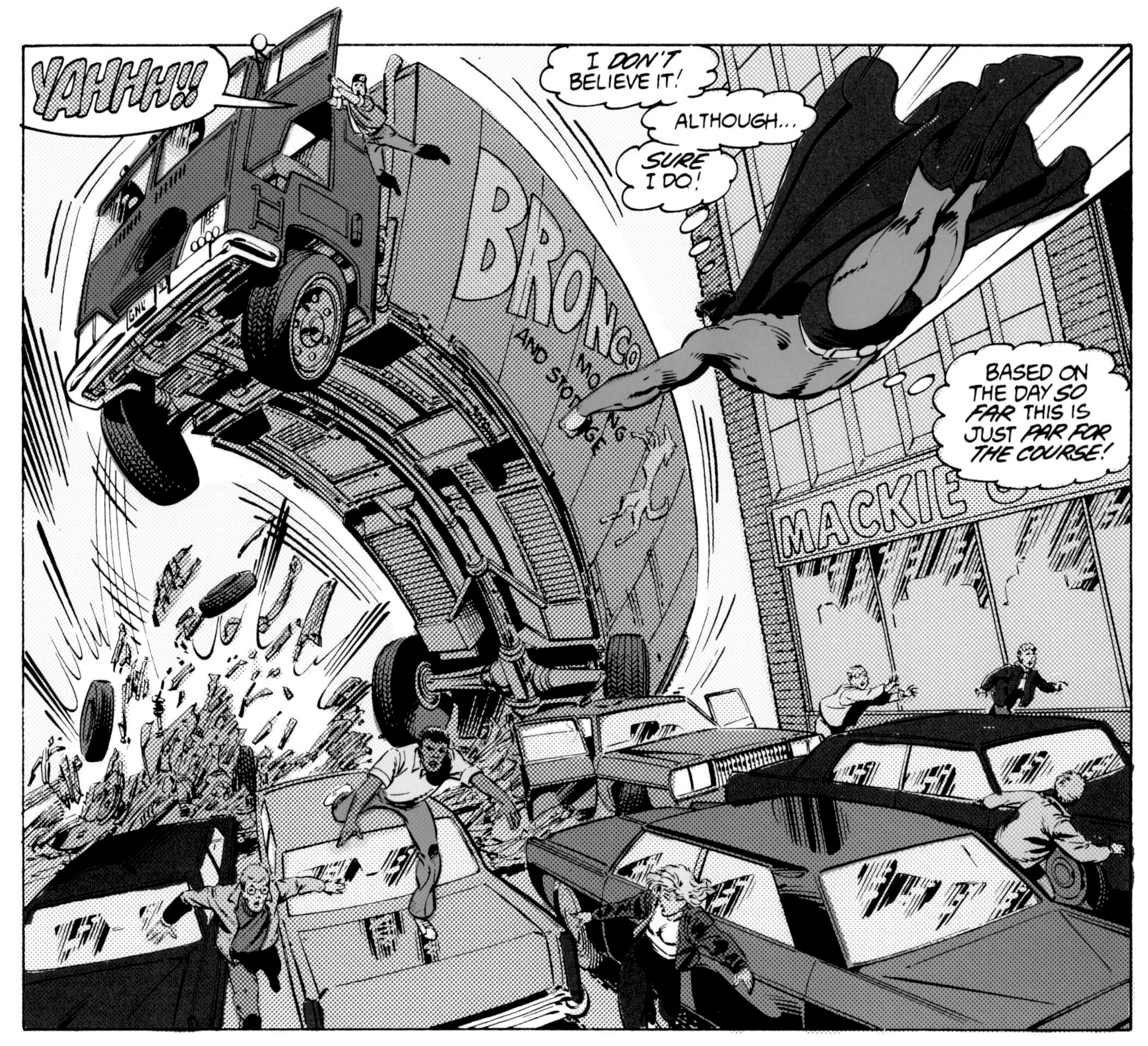

YAHHH!!
I DON'T BELIEVE IT!
ALTHOUGH...
SURE I DO!
BRONCO
BASED ON THE DAY SO FAR THIS IS JUST PAR FOR THE COURSE!
MACKIE

HOLD ON, SIR.
I'VE GOT YOU.
YOU'RE SAFE.
BUT I'M AFRAID I MAY HAVE TO BREAK YOUR TRUCK IF I'M TO STOP IT!
AH!
FINALLY!!
THE VERY MAN I'VE BEEN WAITING FOR!
BEN, HONEY, WHAT'RE Y'ALL...

SILENCE!
YOUR USEFULNESS TO ME IS AT AN END!
RETURN TO THE FORM IN WHICH I FOUND YOU!
BE
AND NOW...
GREETINGS, SUPERMAN! AT LAST WE MEET, FACE TO FACE!
DeROY!
SO HE IS BEHIND ALL THIS!
BETTER NOT LET ON THAT WE'VE ALREADY MET! WHATEVER HIS POWERS, HE DOESN'T SEEM TO REALIZE I'M CLARK KENT.
YOU'RE A LITTLE TOO PLEASED TO SEE ME, STRANGER...
CONSIDERING WHAT YOU'VE BEEN UP TO.
NOT AT ALL, SUPERMAN. ALL THIS WAS FOR YOUR BENEFIT.
TO LURE YOU INTO THE OPEN...
AND NOW YOU'RE HERE...
I HAVE NO FURTHER NEED OF THIS CUMBERSOME DISGUISE!
WHAT IN...???
WHO ARE YOU!?!?
POINK!
13

MY *REAL* NAME WOULD NEVER *TRANSLATE* INTO YOUR CLUMSY EARTH LANGUAGES.
ALL YOU NEED TO KNOW IS THAT I'M FROM A *PARALLEL DIMENSION*.
YOU'D CALL IT... THE *FIFTH DIMENSION*!
AND I'VE BEEN *OBSERVING* YOUR PUNY LITTLE *THIRD DIMENSION* FOR QUITE SOME TIME NOW.
LONG ENOUGH TO KNOW MY SUPERIOR *5-D BRAIN* WILL MAKE ME THE MOST *POWERFUL* BEING ON THIS PLANET.
ALL *YOU* HAVE TO DO, SUPERMAN, IS *STOP ME*!
STOP... Y...?
YES.
YOU SEE, I'M A *GAMESTER*, SUPERMAN. A *GAMBLER*.
AND I THINK *YOU* CAN PROVIDE ME WITH SOME OF THE *CHALLENGE* MY OWN WORLD HAS *LOST*!
OF COURSE... IT WON'T BE *EASY* FOR YOU.
WITH MY *POWERS* I CAN *ALTER YOU* AT WILL!
I CAN MAKE YOU *OLD*...
OR *FAT*...
OR *STUPID*...
...*DAHR*...
OR JUST... *STRANGE*...

BUT THAT'S TOO EASY!
TELL YOU WHAT I'LL DO, SUPERMAN. I'LL MAKE THIS FAIR.
I'LL CHALLENGE YOU TO THE NAME GAME.
ALL YOU HAVE TO DO IS GET ME TO WRITE, SPELL, OR SAY MY NAME BACKWARDS!
THAT'S ALL, HM? UNFORTUNATELY, ACCORDING TO YOU, YOUR NAME WON'T TRANSLATE INTO ANY HUMAN TONGUE!
TRUE ENOUGH. TRUE ENOUGH.
BUT I DO WANT YOU TO HAVE A SPORTING CHANCE, SUPERMAN.
COME FLY LEXAIR
SO...LET'S MAKE UP A NAME!
RIGHT HERE AND NOW!
HE... HE TRANSFORMED THAT BILLBOARD ILLUSTRATION INTO A REAL TYPEWRITER!
THERE MUST BE NO LIMIT TO HIS POWERS!!
THERE YOU ARE, SUPERMAN! MIX-YEZ-PITTLE-ICK!!
FROM NOW ON I'M MISTER MXYZPTLK!!
mxyzptlk
GET ME TO USE IT BACKWARDS, AND I'LL RETURN TO MY HOME DIMENSION...
AND ALL THE EFFECTS OF MY VISIT WILL VANISH WITH ME!

AND SO FAR THOSE EFFECTS HAVE BEEN PIDDLING!
TIME TO GET SERIOUS, I THINK!
SNIK! SNAK!
OH MY GOD!
HE'S ANIMATED THE DAILY PLANET BUILDING!!
MXYZPTLK...
STOP!! THERE ARE HUNDREDS OF PEOPLE IN THAT BUILDING!
WITH MY X-RAY VISION I CAN SEE THEM BEING TOSSED ABOUT LIKE CONFETTI IN A BOX!
OH, FIDDLE FADDLE! YOU 3-D LIFEFORMS ARE A DIME A DOZEN!
KLTPZ
HE'S... TEASING ME! SINGING PART OF HIS "NAME" BACKWARDS!
BUT...
WHAT IN BLAZES CAN I DO!?! HOW DO I STOP THE PLANET BUILDING...
WITHOUT KILLING PEOPLE INSIDE IT??

OH, GREAT!
MXYZPTLK IMBUED THE BUILDING WITH A CHILD'S MENTALITY!
DAILY PLANET
WLEX
IT'S MAKING A GRAB FOR THE WLEX BLIMP!
IT THINKS IT'S SOME KIND OF TOY!
GOT TO PUSH IT OUT OF HIS REACH!
WAAHH
WAA
WAA
OH NO!
THE BUILDING'S THROWING A TANTRUM!
AND ITS TEARS ARE CAUSING A FLASH FLOOD!
HAHAHAHAHA

HEY, SUPERMAN!
CHECK IT OUT!
KLTPZYX
M
WHAT'S HE UP TO NOW?
HE'S SPELLING HIS NAME BACKWARDS WITH SMOKE LETTERS...
AS SOON AS THAT "M" IS IN PLACE...
OOPS!
TOO BAD, SUPES!
KLTPZYXW
BLAST HIM! HE INVERTED THE "M" AT THE LAST INSTANT, MAKING IT A "W".
WAIT A SECOND!
INVERTED!!
THAT'S THE ANSWER!
WHERE'S HE GONE?
SUPERMAN!
YOU SHOW YOURSELF RIGHT NOW OR I'LL CHANGE THIS WHOLE CITY INTO A PEPPERONI PIZZA!
RIGHT HERE, MXYZPTLK.
THAT'S MISTER MXYZPTLK TO YOU, PUNK.
WHAT ARE YOU DOING WITH MY TYPE-WRITER?
mxyzptlk
CALLING YOUR BLUFF, MXYZPTLK.

YOU'VE BEEN MAKING ALL THIS NOISE ABOUT BEING FAIR.
CHALLENGING ME TO YOUR SO-CALLED "NAME GAME".
BUT "MXYZPTLK" ISN'T A NAME! A NAME IS SOMETHING THAT REPRESENTS A PERSON, IT'S NOT JUST LETTERS.
ALL YOU DID WAS HIT A BUNCH OF TYPEWRITER KEYS AT RANDOM.
FOR "MXYZPTLK" TO BE A REAL NAME IT WOULD HAVE TO HAVE BEEN CREATED DELIBERATELY.
I'M BETTING YOU CAN'T REPEAT YOUR RANDOM STRIKING TO PRODUCE THE SAME SEQUENCE OF LETTERS!
OH, WHAT POPPYCOCK!
LOOK!
IT'S EAS...
KLIK KLAK
kltpzyxm
KLIK KLAKETTY KLAK
EEP!
KLTPZYXM!!
IT CAN'T BE!
I USED MY MAGIC TO MAKE SURE I'D HIT THE RIGHT KEYS!!
BUT YOU DIDN'T.
SO LONG, MXYZPTLK!
ALL RIGHT, SUPERMAN.
YOU WIN THIS ONE!
AND I'LL KEEP MY WORD AND LEAVE!
BUT I'LL BE BACK!
COUNT ON IT, SUPERMAN!

"COUNT ON IT!!"
SO... HE'S GONE, SUPERMAN...
BUT NOT FOR GOOD?
NO... BUT FOR AT LEAST 90 DAYS, I'D SAY.
I TALKED TO SOME OF THE THEORETICAL PHYSICS BOYS OVER AT THE UNIVERSITY OF METROPOLIS.
THEY SAY THAT'S THE NEXT TIME THERE WILL BE AN OPTIMUM TRANSFER INTERFACE BETWEEN US AND THE FIFTH DIMENSION.
BUT... HOW ARE YOU, LOIS?
STILL... OFF.
CAN'T QUITE PUT IT INTO WORDS.
COMING TO MY SENSES IN A DEPARTMENT STORE WINDOW DRESSED IN A BIKINI...
WELL... GIVEN THAT THE LAST THING I REMEMBERED BEFORE THAT WAS TURNING TO SPEAK TO CLARK KENT IN THE CITY ROOM...
IT WAS A BIT... UN-NERVING, SUPERMAN.
UNNERVING...
YES. I GUESS THAT WOULD BE A WORD FOR IT. THE PHYSICAL EFFECTS OF MISTER MXYZPTLK'S VISIT ARE ALL GONE...
YOU'RE HUMAN AGAIN, THE PLANET BUILDING IS BACK IN PLACE...
THAT BUCKING BRONCO TRUCK IS JUST A TRUCK AGAIN.
BUT THE PSYCHIATRIC WING OF THIS HOSPITAL MAY HAVE TO OPEN A NEW WARD TO DEAL WITH ALL THE TRAUMA MXYZPTLK UNLEASHED.
THE THINGS HE DID LEFT DEEPER SCARS THAN JUST PHYSICAL INJURY.
I'LL TELL THE WORLD!
BUT... I'M STILL NOT SURE I UNDERSTAND JUST HOW YOU GOT RID OF HIM.
THAT WAS THE EASY PART, ONCE I FIGURED IT OUT.
THE GIANT TYPEWRITER WORKED JUST LIKE A REAL ONE.
I SIMPLY RE-WIRED THE INSIDES AT SUPER-SPEED. WHEN HE HIT THE "M" KEY IT MADE A "K", THE "X" MADE AN "Z", AND SO ON.
YOU SEE, I WAS DEPENDING ON HIM TO CHEAT, TO USE HIS POWERS TO STRIKE THE CORRECT KEYS "AT RANDOM".
AND WHEN HE DID...
M-X-Y-Z-P-T-L-K CAME OUT K-L-T-P-Z-Y-X-M!
AND HE LOST!

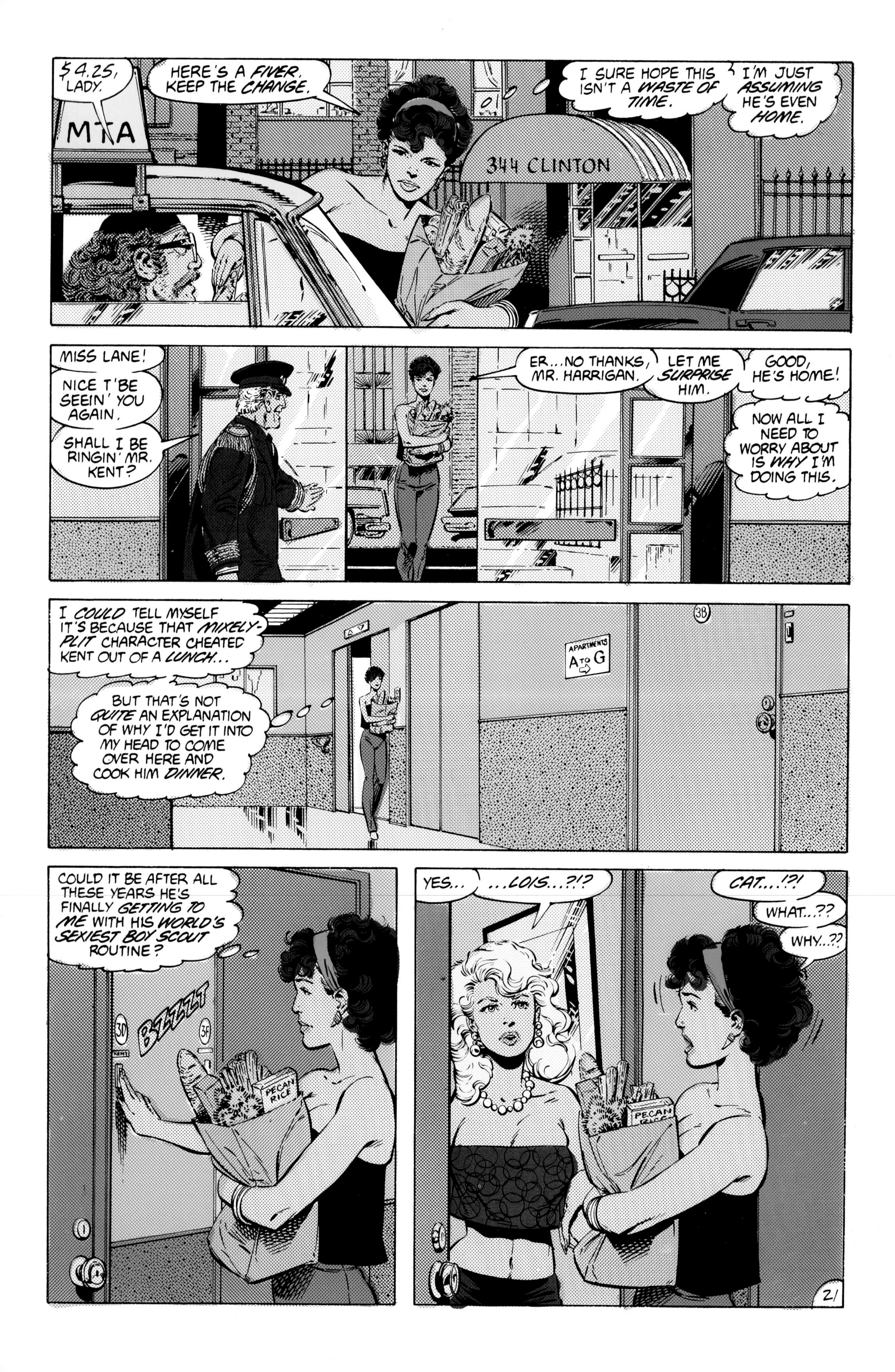

$4.25, LADY.
HERE'S A FIVER. KEEP THE CHANGE.
MTA
344 CLINTON
I SURE HOPE THIS ISN'T A WASTE OF TIME.
I'M JUST ASSUMING HE'S EVEN HOME.
MISS LANE!
NICE T'BE SEEIN' YOU AGAIN.
SHALL I BE RINGIN' MR. KENT?
ER...NO THANKS, MR. HARRIGAN.
LET ME SURPRISE HIM.
GOOD, HE'S HOME!
NOW ALL I NEED TO WORRY ABOUT IS WHY I'M DOING THIS.
I COULD TELL MYSELF IT'S BECAUSE THAT MIXELYPLIT CHARACTER CHEATED KENT OUT OF A LUNCH...
BUT THAT'S NOT QUITE AN EXPLANATION OF WHY I'D GET IT INTO MY HEAD TO COME OVER HERE AND COOK HIM DINNER.
APARTMENTS A TO G
3B
COULD IT BE AFTER ALL THESE YEARS HE'S FINALLY GETTING TO ME WITH HIS WORLD'S SEXIEST BOY SCOUT ROUTINE?
BZZZZT
3D
3F
PECAN RICE
YES...
...LOIS...?!?
CAT...!?!
WHAT...??
WHY...??

CLARKIE'S IN THE *SHOWER*.
I WAS JUST GOING TO FIX HIM A NICE *DINNER*.
LOIS! THAT'S NOT WHAT *YOU'RE* HERE FOR, IS IT?
WHAT...??
OH...
NO!
I WAS... JUST... *PASSING*...
OH, *GOOD!*
THEN YOU CAN *KEEP* PASSING, YES?
I...
I...
PECAN RICE
WHO WAS THAT AT THE *DOOR*, CAT?
OH, NOBODY *IMPORTANT*.
SOMEBODY WHO GOT OFF ON THE WRONG *FLOOR* WITHOUT *REALIZING*.
NOW, C'MON, CLARKIE. DINNER'S *HOT*...
AND *SO* AM *I*!
...CAT...

SUPERMAN 9 Published monthly by DC Comics Inc., 666 Fifth Avenue, New York, NY 10103. POSTMASTER: Send address changes to SUPERMAN, DC Comics Inc., Subscription Dept. P.O. Box 1981, New York, NY 10185. Annual subscription rate $9.00. Outside U.S.A. $11.00 in U.S. funds. Advertising Representative: Print Advertising Representatives Inc., 355 Lexington Avenue, New York, NY 10017. (212) 391-1400. Printed in U.S.A. DC Comics Inc. A Warner Communications Company

HEY, LOOK! HE'S GOIN' INTA TH' DIAMOND EXCHANGE BUILDING.
YEAH!
D'YOU S'POSE THERE'S...
...TROUBLE OF SOME KIND, SUPERMAN?
WE'VE BEEN VERY WORRIED, OF COURSE, WITH THE STAR OF ZAHARAIN HERE.
SECURITY HAS BEEN MORE THAN DOUBLED TO DISCOURAGE ANY WOULD-BE THIEVES...
BUT... IF YOU'VE HEARD SOMETHING...
SOMETHING WE SHOULD KNOW ABOUT...
AH...?
SUPERMAN?
S-SUPERMAN...?!?

HISSSSSSSS SSSSSSSS
HAK
KOF
KOF
KOF
MEAN-WHILE...
OPEN THIS WRETCHED THING? IT'S BEEN LYING ON YOUR DESK FOR A WEEK OR MORE.
OH, YES!
IT GOT BURIED UNDER ALL MY RESEARCH MATERIAL FOR THE CLETUS POWELL STORY, AND I FORGOT ALL ABOUT IT.
PEAKED YOUR CURIOSITY, HAS IT, LOIS?
WELL, YOU KNOW WHAT THEY SAY ABOUT "PLAIN BROWN WRAPPERS," KENT.
HALF THE PLANET STAFF HAS BEEN WONDERING WHAT'S IN IT.
MURPHY EVEN STARTED A POOL.
V-E DAY
GUESS I'D BETTER PUT EVERYONE OUT OF THEIR MISERY THEN, HM?
TO BE HONEST I HAVEN'T THE FAINTEST IDEA MYSELF WHAT...
CRACKLE! RRIPPPP
?!?
SCRAP BOOK™
3

A SCRAP-BOOK...!?!
HOW... ORDINARY!
IS IT AT LEAST A JUICY SCRAP-BOOK?
APPARENTLY NOT.
SEE FOR YOURSELF, LOIS.
HUH!
IT'S JUST A BUNCH OF CLIPPINGS ABOUT AVERTED CATASTROPHES!
CONCORDE LA SAFELY AFTER LANDING GEAR MALFUNCTION
BEAR AND BOY UNHARMED IN MYSTERY RESCUE
GRIZZLY
SCIENTISTS BAFFLED AS FALLING SATELLITE CHANGES COURSE
FREAK RAINFALL BRINGS DROUGHT RELIEF
NO INJURIES AS BLAZE VANISHES
FERRY REMAINS AFLOAT AFTER
OR IS IT?
HMM. ABOUT HALFWAY THROUGH IT TURNS INTO STORIES ON SUPERMAN!
IT DOES...?
LET ME...
HM??
M.I.T. SPACE STATION REGAINS ORBIT
ER... HOLD ON TO THAT BOOK FOR ME, WILL YOU, LOIS?
I JUST... REMEMBERED SOMETHING I HAVE TO DO.
OR MORE EXACTLY...
SOMETHING SUPERMAN HAS TO DO!
FORBES

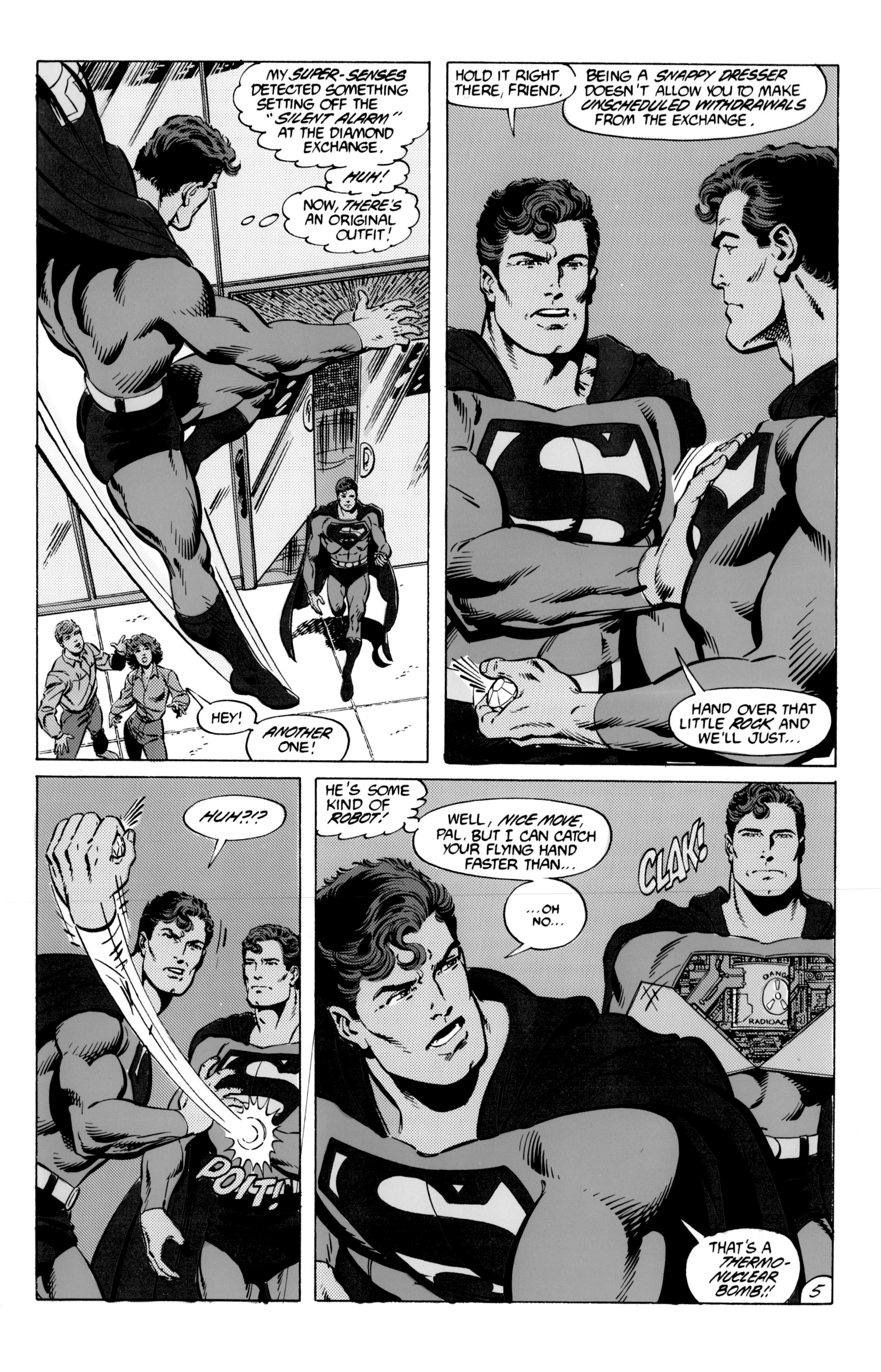
MY SUPER-SENSES DETECTED SOMETHING SETTING OFF THE "SILENT ALARM" AT THE DIAMOND EXCHANGE.
HUH!
NOW, THERE'S AN ORIGINAL OUTFIT!
HEY!
ANOTHER ONE!
HOLD IT RIGHT THERE, FRIEND.
BEING A SNAPPY DRESSER DOESN'T ALLOW YOU TO MAKE UNSCHEDULED WITHDRAWALS FROM THE EXCHANGE.
HAND OVER THAT LITTLE ROCK AND WE'LL JUST...
HUH?!?
POIT!
HE'S SOME KIND OF ROBOT!
WELL, NICE MOVE, PAL, BUT I CAN CATCH YOUR FLYING HAND FASTER THAN...
...OH NO...
CLAK!
THAT'S A THERMO-NUCLEAR BOMB!!

ONLY A FEW SECONDS FOR ME TO ACT!

GOT TO GET IT AWAY FROM THE CITY...

MEANWHILE...
A FARMHOUSE JUST OUTSIDE SMALLVILLE, KANSAS.
...and when I dreeeeeeamm...
I dream of YOOOOOOOU...
...maybe someday you will come truuuue...
Lahh dahh dahh deeeee... dahh dah dah deeeee...
Lahh dah dah dee dah dah dah...
?!?
8

THIRTY MINUTES LATER...
THE GREAT MOJAVE DESERT...
UH-UHHHHH-H
HOW...
UNHH...
ABOUT...
THAT...?
I'M NOT DEAD.
I HURT TOO MUCH TO BE DEAD.
BUT...
CAN'T WASTE TIME HERE... GOT TO GET BACK TO METROPOLIS...
GET ON TOP OF THIS CASE...
SO...
UP, UP AND...

THAT THE LAST OF 'EM, GREG?
YES 'M, CAP'N.
NINE IN ALL, COUNTING THE TWO WHO WANDERED IN AFTER "SUPERMAN" CAME OUT.
NINE DEAD...
ALL OF METROPOLIS THREATENED...
AND ALL FOR A LUMP OF CRUSHED COAL THAT ONLY HAS VALUE BECAUSE WE SAY IT DOES.
THE GUY'S AS NUTS AS ALL TH' GOTHAM PAPERS SAY HE IS.
CAPTAIN SAWYER...
CAPTAIN, I'M TOBY RAYNES, FROM THE METROPOLIS STAR.
ISN'T IT UNUSUAL FOR YOUR SPECIAL CRIMES UNIT TO BE INVOLVED IN THIS HEIST?
DON'T YOU USUALLY CONCERN YOURSELF MOSTLY WITH SO-CALLED SUPER-VILLAINS?
WHICH IS JUST WHAT WE SEEM TO BE DEALING WITH HERE, MS. RAYNES.
HOLD THAT LAST BODY FOR A SEC, GREG.
LET 'ER THROUGH, BOYS.
SEE FOR YOURSELF, MS. RAYNES.
THE DISTORTION OF THE FACE IS CAUSED BY THE SAME STUFF THAT KILLED HER.
IN THIS CASE, A GAS THAT CAUSES ALMOST INSTANTANEOUS MUSCULAR CONSTRICTION. KILLS IN ABOUT THIRTY SECONDS, AND LEAVES US WITH THE CALLING CARD OF...

...THE JOKER!
SUPERMAN!
MAN, AM I GLAD TO SEE YOU IN ONE PIECE!
AFTER ALL THE EYEWITNESSES TOLD ME YOU FLEW OFF WITH AN ATOM-BOMB...
AND WE SAW THAT BIG FLARE IN THE SKY...
YES...
WELL, I'VE SEEN BETTER DAYS, CAPTAIN.
NOW... MAYBE YOU'D BETTER FILL ME IN ON WHAT YOU'VE LEARNED HERE.
THAT SHOULD TAKE ABOUT EIGHT SECONDS.
NINE DEAD... ALL GRINNING THEIR FACES OFF... AND THE STAR OF ZAHARAIN STOLEN.
A BUSY HOUR, EVEN FOR THE JOKER!
IF IT IS THE JOKER, MAGGIE, AND NOT SOME COPYCAT.
GOTHAM CITY IS HIS USUAL TURF-- AND HIS SOLE MOTIVATION SEEMS TO BE VEXING THE BATMAN.
SO WHAT'S HE DOING IN METROPOLIS?
THE BATMAN COULD ANSWER THAT ONE BETTER THAN I CAN, SUPERMAN.
MAYBE YOU SHOULD CALL UP YOUR POINTY-EARED PAL AND ASK HIM.
MM... UNFORTUNATELY HE AND I ARE NOT EXACTLY "PALS", MARGARET.
OUR METHODS TEND TO GET ON EACH OTHER'S NERVES.
STILL A QUICK TRIP TO GOTHAM MIGHT BE WORTH THE...
OW!
SUPERMAN!
WHAT'S WRONG??
11

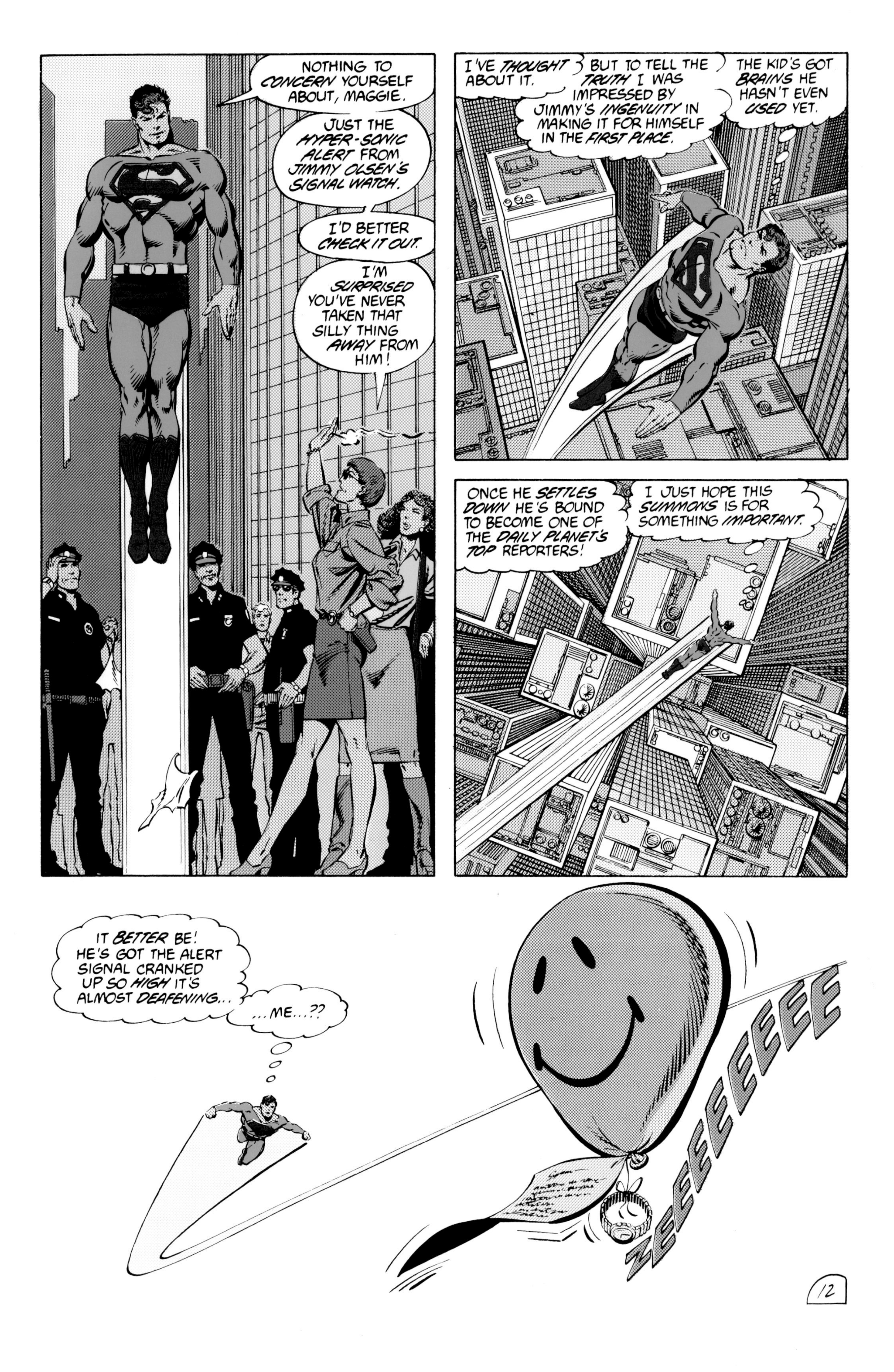
NOTHING TO CONCERN YOURSELF ABOUT, MAGGIE.
JUST THE HYPER-SONIC ALERT FROM JIMMY OLSEN'S SIGNAL WATCH.
I'D BETTER CHECK IT OUT.
I'M SURPRISED YOU'VE NEVER TAKEN THAT SILLY THING AWAY FROM HIM!
I'VE THOUGHT ABOUT IT.
BUT TO TELL THE TRUTH I WAS IMPRESSED BY JIMMY'S INGENUITY IN MAKING IT FOR HIMSELF IN THE FIRST PLACE.
THE KID'S GOT BRAINS HE HASN'T EVEN USED YET.
ONCE HE SETTLES DOWN HE'S BOUND TO BECOME ONE OF THE DAILY PLANET'S TOP REPORTERS!
I JUST HOPE THIS SUMMONS IS FOR SOMETHING IMPORTANT.
IT BETTER BE! HE'S GOT THE ALERT SIGNAL CRANKED UP SO HIGH IT'S ALMOST DEAFENING...
...ME...??
ZEEEEEEEEE

SUPERMAN...
BY NOW YOU KNOW I MEAN BUSINESS. TO DISSUADE YOU FROM ATTEMPTING TO STOP MY LEAVING YOUR FAIR CITY, I HAVE BORROWED THREE OF YOUR FRIENDS.
LOIS LANE, JIMMY OLSEN, AND PERRY WHITE ARE IN SEALED, LEAD-LINED COFFINS IN VARIOUS PLACES AROUND METROPOLIS.
YOUR CHOICE IS OBVIOUS: COME AFTER ME, OR SAVE YOUR FRIENDS.
OH--THEY EACH HAVE LESS THAN HALF AN HOUR OF AIR.
THE JOKER
HAHAHAHAHAHA
BLAST!!
THIS IS TOO RICH!
IT REALLY IS!

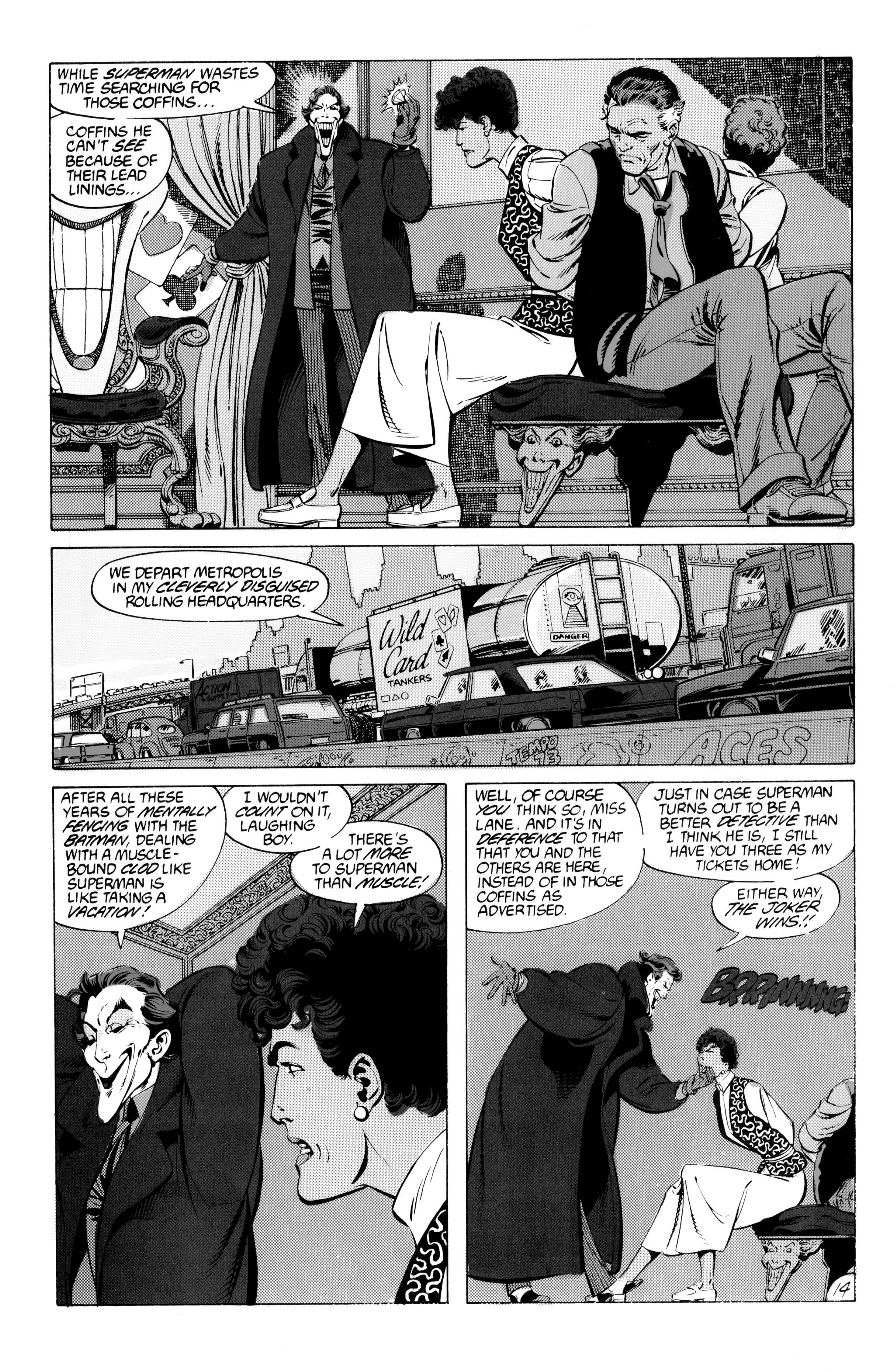
WHILE SUPERMAN WASTES TIME SEARCHING FOR THOSE COFFINS...
COFFINS HE CAN'T SEE BECAUSE OF THEIR LEAD LININGS...
WE DEPART METROPOLIS IN MY CLEVERLY DISGUISED ROLLING HEADQUARTERS.
Wild Card TANKERS
ACTION SUPPLY
DANGER
ACES
AFTER ALL THESE YEARS OF MENTALLY FENCING WITH THE BATMAN, DEALING WITH A MUSCLE-BOUND CLOD LIKE SUPERMAN IS LIKE TAKING A VACATION!
I WOULDN'T COUNT ON IT, LAUGHING BOY.
THERE'S A LOT MORE TO SUPERMAN THAN MUSCLE!
WELL, OF COURSE YOU THINK SO, MISS LANE. AND IT'S IN DEFERENCE TO THAT THAT YOU AND THE OTHERS ARE HERE, INSTEAD OF IN THOSE COFFINS AS ADVERTISED.
JUST IN CASE SUPERMAN TURNS OUT TO BE A BETTER DETECTIVE THAN I THINK HE IS, I STILL HAVE YOU THREE AS MY TICKETS HOME!
EITHER WAY, THE JOKER WINS!!
BRRINNNNG!

BLAST IT ALL, DOOLEY! HOW MANY TIMES DO I HAVE TO TELL YOU NOT TO INTERRUPT ME WHEN I'M GLOATING?
WHAT?
WHAT?!?
...OH NO...
DANGER
HI, JOKER.
NO PUN INTENDED.
TAKE A SEAT, SMILEY. IT WON'T BE A MOMENT BEFORE WE REACH...

D0576384
THE METROPOLITAN MAXIMUM SECURITY INTERNMENT CENTER, ON STRYKER'S ISLAND.
THE LOCAL AUTHORITIES ARE READY TO TAKE CARE OF YOU AND YOUR BOYS UNTIL THE GOTHAM POLICE COME TO GET YOU.
MMS
Wild Card TANKERS
SHUUNG!!
Wild Card TANKERS
AND NOW...
I THINK THAT'S GAME, SET, AND MATCH, JOKER.
HOW ABOUT YOU?
16